Y0-CDP-714

An Educational Coloring Book
of

SOUTHEAST INDIANS

EDITOR
Linda Spizzirri

ILLUSTRATIONS
Peter M. Spizzirri

COVER ART
Peter M. Spizzirri

CONTENTS

An Educational Coloring Book of SOUTHEAST INDIANS • Published by SPIZZIRRI PUBLISHING, INC., P.O. BOX 9397, RAPID CITY, SOUTH DAKOTA 57709. No part of this publication may be reproduced by any means without the express written consent of the publisher. All national and international rights reserved on the entire contents of this publication.
Printed in U.S.A.

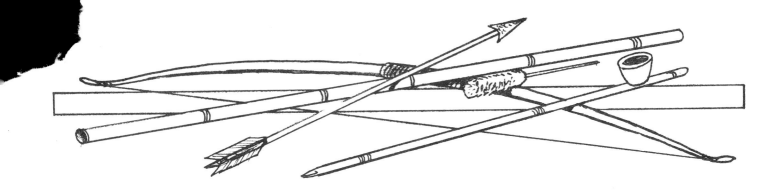

TRIBE NAME:	TIMUCUA OR UTINA
LANGUAGE:	MUSKOGEAN
WHERE THEY LIVED:	FLORIDA
KIND OF HOUSE:	CIRCULAR-SHAPED, WOODEN, POLE FRAME WITH PALMETTO THATCHED WALLS AND ROOF
WHAT THEY ATE:	CORN, ALLIGATORS, DEER, BUFFALO, SMALL GAME, SHELLFISH, WILD FRUIT, ARROWROOT BREAD
INTERESTING FACTS:	The Timucua were a group of tribes that occupied most of Northern Florida. They built fortified villages surrounded by a stockade that had a guard house at the entrance. Tribe members tattooed their bodies with various red, blue, and black designs. The men tied their long hair into a knot and used it to hold arrows while they were hunting. They were experts at boat building and sailing. They traveled the Florida coast and to Cuba trading canoes and other products.

WARRIORS

2

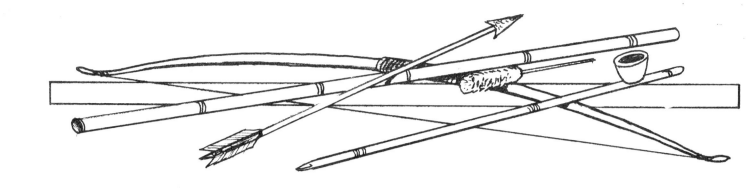

TRIBE NAME:	CHEROKEE
LANGUAGE:	IROQUOIAN
WHERE THEY LIVED:	TENNESSEE
KIND OF HOUSE:	ROUND SHAPE. POLE FRAME COVERED WITH WOVEN MATS AND PLASTERED WITH CLAY BOTH INSIDE AND OUT
WHAT THEY ATE:	CORN, SQUASH, SWEET POTATOES, BEANS, GAME AND GATHERED FOOD
INTERESTING FACTS:	The Cherokee were the largest of the southeastern tribes and they were members of the "Five Civilized Tribes." Each village was ruled by a chief and a council of wise men. Women were highly respected and often helped in the choice of a new chief or served as priestess' in special ceremonies. Each year, as the new corn ripened, the tribe would celebrate with feasting, dancing, and games. Old differences were forgotten, friendships were renewed, and new fires were laid to start the new year.

CORN DANCE CEREMONY

6

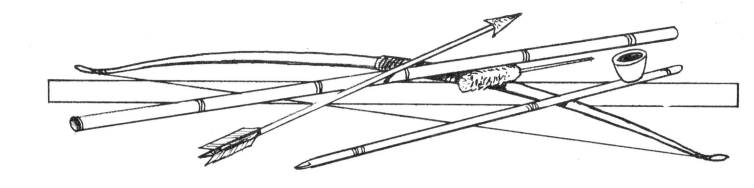

TRIBE NAME:	CHEROKEE
LANGUAGE:	IROQUOIAN
WHERE THEY LIVED:	TENNESSEE
KIND OF HOUSE:	ROUND SHAPE. POLE FRAME COVERED WITH WOVEN MATS AND PLASTERED WITH CLAY BOTH INSIDE AND OUT
WHAT THEY ATE:	CORN, SQUASH, SWEET POTATOES, BEANS, GAME AND GATHERED FOOD
INTERESTING FACTS:	The Cherokee were the largest of the southeastern tribes and they were members of the "Five Civilized Tribes." Each village was ruled by a chief and a council of wise men. Women were highly respected and often helped in the choice of a new chief or served as priestess' in special ceremonies. Each year, as the new corn ripened, the tribe would celebrate with feasting, dancing, and games. Old differences were forgotten, friendships were renewed, and new fires were laid to start the new year.

CORN DANCE CEREMONY

6

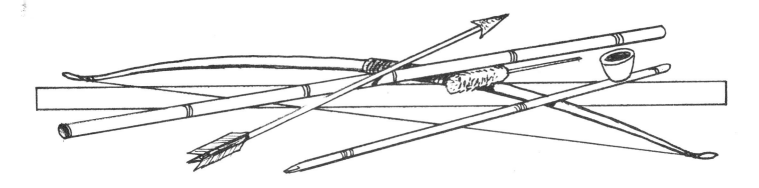

TRIBE NAME:	TUTELO
LANGUAGE:	SIOUAN
WHERE THEY LIVED:	VIRGINIA
KIND OF HOUSE:	ARCHED ROOF RECTANGLE WITH MAT WALLS AND BARK ROOF
WHAT THEY ATE:	CORN, WILD FOODS THEY COULD GATHER, FISH, BUFFALO, ELK, BEAR, AND SMALL GAME
INTERESTING FACTS:	The Tutelo were noted for their custom of "spirit adoption." When a member of a tribe died, the family adopted another tribe member of the same age and sex. The possessions and responsibilities of the departed became those of the person that was adopted. For one night during the ceremony, the adopted person acted as if they were the departed spirit who returned so that the family could honor and feast with them one more time.

SPIRIT ADOPTION

8

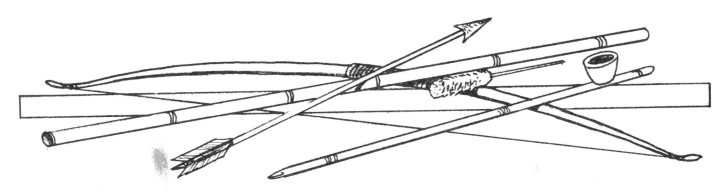

TRIBE NAME:	CREEK
LANGUAGE:	MUSKOGEAN
WHERE THEY LIVED:	ALABAMA AND GEORGIA
KIND OF HOUSE:	HOUSES WERE ARRANGED IN GROUP. (SEE INTERESTING FACTS:)
WHAT THEY ATE:	CORN, BEANS, PUMPKINS, SQUASH, SWEET POTATOES, LARGE AND SMALL GAME, FISH, ROOTS, NUTS, AND FRUIT
INTERESTING FACTS:	The Creek Indians were so named because of their practice of always building their villages along a stream or creek. They were one of the "Five Civilized Tribes," and the major tribe of the Creek Confederacy which included many of the smaller tribes around them. A Creek family home was a group of four different rectangular structures. All had wooden, pole frames and bark roofs. The winter and summer houses had walls of interwoven branches or reeds that were plastered with mud. The summer house was also used as a guest house. Half of the storehouse had no walls and half was enclosed. The warehouse had just a roof and was open on all sides.

A CREEK VILLAGE

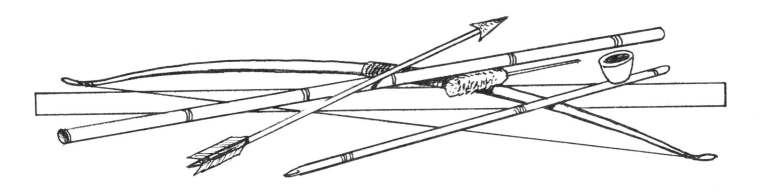

TRIBE NAME:	CATAWBA
LANGUAGE:	SIOUAN
WHERE THEY LIVED:	NORTH AND SOUTH CAROLINA
KIND OF HOUSE:	POLE FRAME, BARK COVERED HUTS
WHAT THEY ATE:	CORN, BEANS, SQUASH, FISH, PIGEONS, BUFFALO, DEER, ELK, AND BEAR
INTERESTING FACTS:	This tribe lived in the Carolinas along the shores of the Catawba River and their name means, "people of the river." The women of the tribe cultivated the fields and cared for the children. The men were great warriors, hunters, and travelers. They traveled into Georgia and as far north as the Great Lakes. Early accounts of this tribe note that they built temples of worship, like their southern neighbors.

TRAVELERS TO FAR LANDS

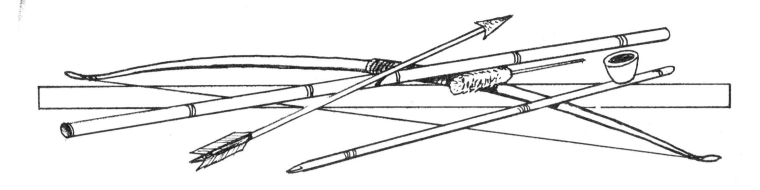

TRIBE NAME:	NATCHEZ
LANGUAGE:	MUSKOGEAN
WHERE THEY LIVED:	MISSISSIPPI, LOUISIANA, AND TEXAS
KIND OF HOUSE:	RECTANGULAR-SHAPED, MUD HOUSE WITH MATS ON THE OUTSIDE AND A THATCHED ROOF
WHAT THEY ATE:	CORN, BEANS, PUMPKINS, MUSH-ROOMS, WATERMELON, PEACHES, WILD RICE, GRAPES, PERSIMMONS, NUTS, BUFFALO, DEER, GAME BIRDS, LARGE AND SMALL FISH
INTERESTING FACTS:	The Natchez were the largest tribe along the lower Mississippi River. Like all southeastern tribes, they were divided into clans. Children were considered members of the mother's clan (family). Mothers trained their daughters and their sons were taught games, hunting, fishing, and warfare by their mother's brothers (uncles). Fathers had little to do with their own children because it was their duty to teach their nephews about Natchez life. It was strictly against the law for any man or woman to marry a member of his or her own clan.

UNCLE TEACHING HIS NEPHEWS

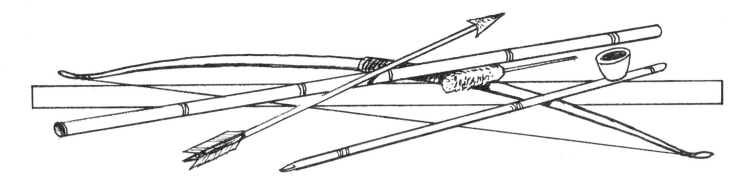

TRIBE NAME:	SEMINOLE
LANGUAGE:	MUSKOGEAN
WHERE THEY LIVED:	FLORIDA
KIND OF HOUSE:	CALLED "CHICKEES." BUILT OF CYPRESS POLES, OPEN-SIDED HOUSE ON STILTS, HAD A PALM LEAF ROOF
WHAT THEY ATE:	CORN, BEANS, SQUASH, FISH, GAME, ALLIGATORS, AND GATHERED FOODS
INTERESTING FACTS:	The Seminoles were not referred to as a tribe until about 1775. They were indians from the Creek Confederacy who fled the wars in Georgia and the Carolinas. Although they retained the Creek culture, they never lived together in large villages. During three different wars, from 1817 to 1858, the government attempted to relocate all of the Seminole Indians to reservations in the west. Some 300 members of the tribe moved deep into the Florida Everglades to avoid this move. They had to develop new skills and crafts to successfully live in the swamps. They developed a shallow canoe that was suited for traveling in the everglades. More than 2000 descendants of these Indians still live in the Florida Everglades today.

LIVING IN THE EVERGLADES

16

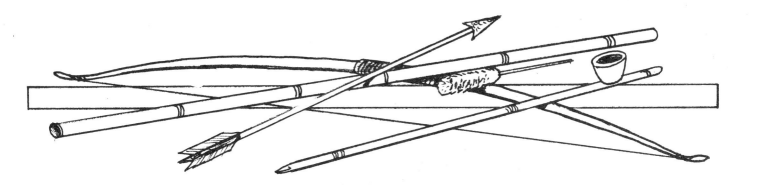

TRIBE NAME:	APALACHEE
LANGUAGE:	MUSKOGEAN
WHERE THEY LIVED:	NORTHWESTERN FLORIDA
KIND OF HOUSE:	WOODEN, POLE FRAME. PALMETTO THATCHED WALLS AND ROOF
WHAT THEY ATE:	CORN, PEAS, BEANS, PUMPKINS AND SQUASH, WILD FRUIT, SEAFOOD, FISH, AND GAME
INTERESTING FACTS:	It is believed that the Apalachee came from somewhere west of the Mississippi and moved into Northwestern Florida around the year of 1300. They brought with them the tradition of building temple mounds, around which they built their towns. Being primarily farmers, they planted large corn fields around the towns. The men of the tribe worked in the fields as well as the women.

TEMPLE MOUND BUILDERS

18

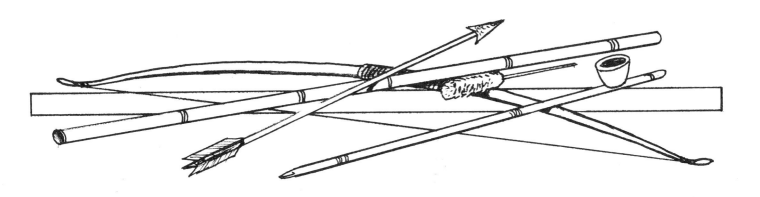

TRIBE NAME:	CHITIMACHA
LANGUAGE:	CHITIMACHAN
WHERE THEY LIVED:	LOUISANA
KIND OF HOUSE:	WOODEN POLE FRAME AND PALMETTO THATCHED WALLS AND ROOF
WHAT THEY ATE:	FISH, TURTLES, SHRIMP, ALLIGATORS, GAME, BEANS, PUMPKINS, MELONS, SWEET POTATOES
INTERESTING FACTS:	The Chitimachan women wove beautiful patterned cane baskets with fitted tops. They were famous for a double-weave method which is mostly lost today. The women also had a great deal of authority in the tribe. They served as medicine women, subchiefs, or even chiefs.
	In addition to the usual weapons, the men used a blow gun and dart for hunting, which enabled them to kill small game from a distance of up to 60 feet.

WEAVING BASKETS

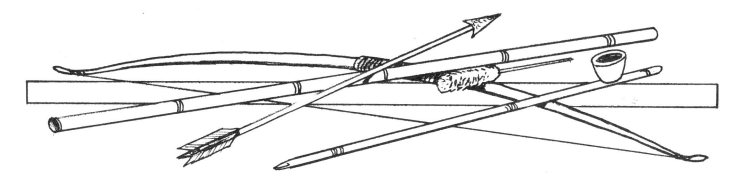

TRIBE NAME:	CHICKASAW
LANGUAGE:	MUSKOGEAN
WHERE THEY LIVED:	MISSISSIPPI
KIND OF HOUSE:	SUMMER: RECTANGULAR, POLE FRAME STRUCTURE WITH WOVEN MAT WALLS AND A BARK ROOF WINTER: CIRCULAR, POLE FRAME STRUCTURE. PINE LOGS WERE COVERED WITH A CLAY AND GRASS PLASTER. THIS WAS EXCAVATED THREE FEET INTO THE GROUND
WHAT THEY ATE:	DEER, BUFFALO, OTHER GAME, AND FISH. STRAWBERRIES, PERSIMMONS, ONIONS, GRAPES, AND HONEY
INTERESTING FACTS:	The Chicasaw were one of the members of the "Five Civilized Tribes." Tradition holds that the Choctaw and Chickasaw were once a single tribe. The women of the tribe had the responsibility of planting crops, food gathering, and doing all household chores. The men went to war, did the hunting, fishing, and building of the houses. They had a unique way of catching fish. They made a mild poison out of green walnut husks and threw it into the lake or pond. They waited for the poison to take effect and as the drugged fish floated to the surface, they would spear them easily.

FISHING WITH SPEARS

22

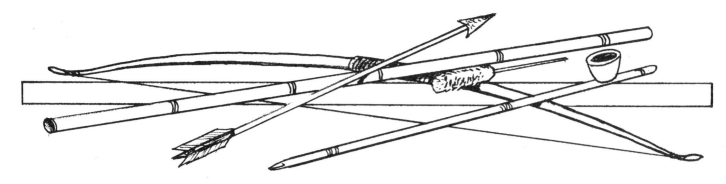

TRIBE NAME:	CHOCTAW
LANGUAGE:	MUSKOGEAN
WHERE THEY LIVED:	MISSISSIPPI AND ALABAMA
KIND OF HOUSE:	WOODEN, POLE FRAMES WITH BARK WALLS AND ROOFS
WHAT THEY ATE:	CORN, BEANS, PUMPKINS, MELONS, DEER, BEAR, SMALL GAME, FISH, FRUIT, NUTS, SEEDS, AND ROOTS
INTERESTING FACTS:	The Choctaw were a peace-loving people that were members of the "Five Civilized Tribes." They believed that disputes should be settled by talking instead of fighting. But, if they were forced to fight, they were strong, fierce warriors.

The Choctaw had unique funeral rites for their dead. When someone died, the body was placed on an elevated platform along with food and utensils needed for the journey to the land of the dead. A fire would be kept burning, by the platform, during the mourning period. The body was then taken down and placed in the "bone house." After a period of time, the bone house became full and all of the bones were removed and buried at one time. Mounds were built over these burial sites. The Choctaw were called "The Mississippi Mound Builders."

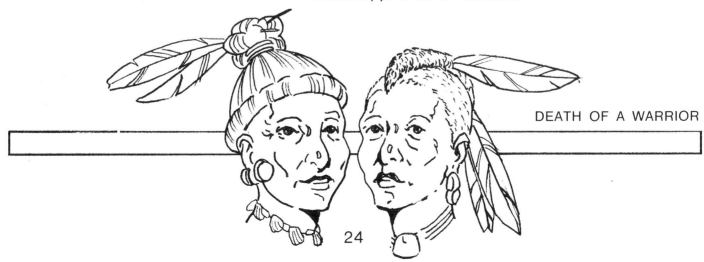

DEATH OF A WARRIOR

24

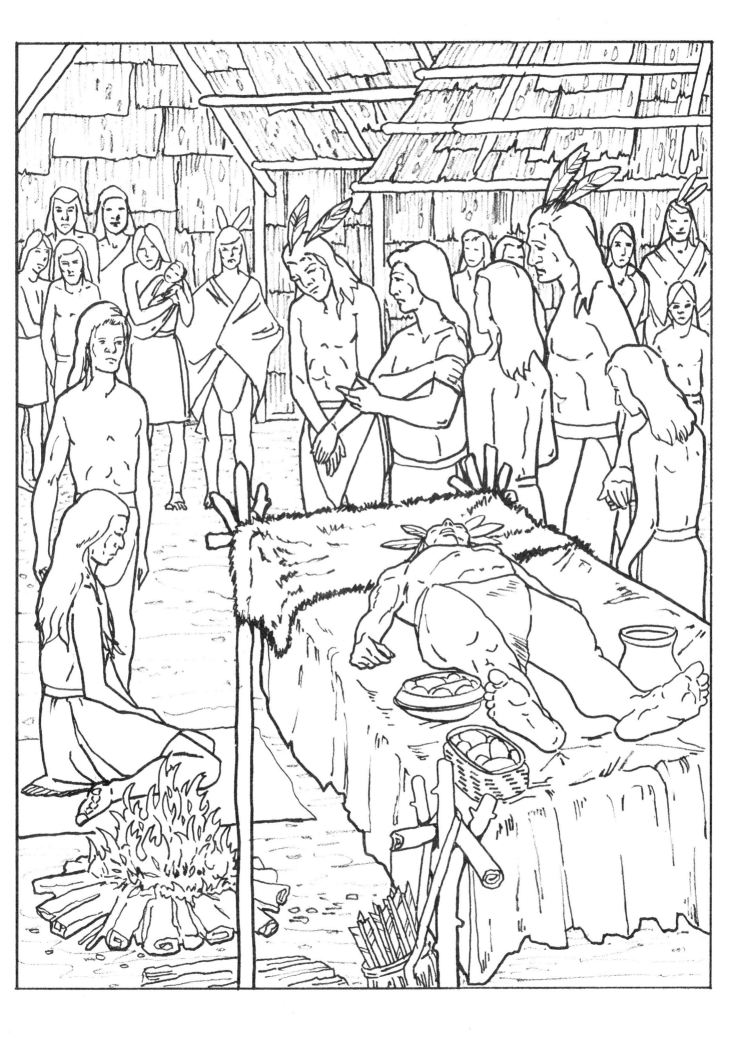

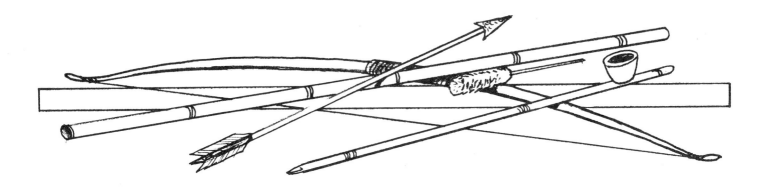

TRIBE NAME:	ATAKAPA
LANGUAGE:	TUNICAN
WHERE THEY LIVED:	LOUISIANA AND TEXAS COAST
KIND OF HOUSE:	ROUND, WOODEN, POLE FRAME STRUC-TURE WITH WOVEN VINE WALLS AND A THATCHED CONICAL ROOF (CONE SHAPED)
WHAT THEY ATE:	FISH, SHELLFISH, WILD PLANTS, SOME CORN, GAME, ALLIGATORS, AND WATER-BIRDS
INTERESTING FACTS:	The Atakapa lived in coastal fishing villages and got most of their food from the ocean. They traded dried fish, shark's teeth, and waterbird feathers with inland tribes for pottery and animal skins. Whenever they caught an alligator, they would cook it whole and have a feast. They used the oil from the alligator as a mosquito repellant and suntan lotion.

HUNTING AN ALLIGATOR

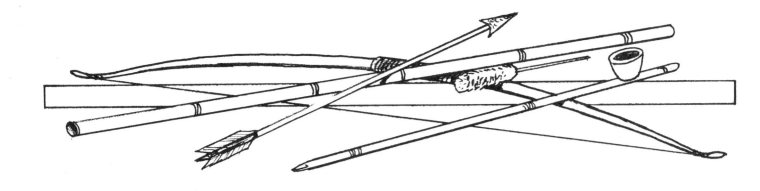

TRIBE NAME:	ALABAMA OR ALIBAMU
LANGUAGE:	MUSKOGEAN
WHERE THEY LIVED:	ALABAMA
KIND OF HOUSE:	WOODEN, POLE FRAME WITH BARK ROOF AND WALLS
WHAT THEY ATE:	CORN, BEANS, PUMPKINS, SQUASH, FISH, AND GAME
INTERESTING FACTS:	A wooden stockade, sealed with mud, protected the typical town of the Alabama. The center of town had an open-air, circular meeting place and a yard for playing "chunky." Chunky is a game where a stone disc is rolled and the players throw a shaft at it. Points were scored by hitting the disc or by coming closest to where it stopped.

PLAYING CHUNKY

28

Educational Coloring Books and
STORY CASSETTES

The only non-fiction coloring book/cassette packages available! The cassettes are not read-alongs. Rather, the educational factual information in the coloring book is utilized and enhanced to create exciting stories. Sound, music, and professional narration stimulate interest and promote reading. Children can color and listen, color alone, or simply listen to the cassette. We are proud to offer these quality products at a reasonable price.

DISPLAY RACKS AVAILABLE. INDIVIDUALLY PACKAGED.

YOUR CHOICE OF 48 TITLES

"ISBN (INTERNATIONAL STANDARD BOOK NUMBER) PREFIX ON ALL BOOKS AND CASSETTES: 0-86545-

No. 082-X	DINOSAURS	No. 161-3	DOGS
No. 083-8	Prehistoric SEA LIFE	No. 162-1	HORSES
No. 084-6	Prehistoric BIRDS	No. 159-1	BIRDS
No. 085-4	CAVE MAN	No. 147-8	PENGUINS
No. 086-2	Prehistoric FISH	No. 098-6	STATE BIRDS
No. 087-0	Prehistoric MAMMALS	No. 163-X	STATE FLOWERS
No. 097-8	Count/Color DINOSAURS	No. 100-1	MAMMALS
No. 089-7	PLAINS INDIANS	No. 101-X	REPTILES
No. 090-0	NORTHEAST INDIANS	No. 158-3	POISONOUS SNAKES
No. 091-9	NORTHWEST INDIANS	No. 102-8	CATS OF THE WILD
NO. 092-7	SOUTHEAST INDIANS	No. 103-6	ENDANGERED SPECIES
No. 093-5	SOUTHWEST INDIANS	No. 157-5	PRIMATES
No. 094-3	CALIFORNIA INDIANS	No. 104-4	ANIMAL GIANTS
No. 153-2	ESKIMOS	No. 148-6	ATLANTIC FISH
No. 152-4	COWBOYS	No. 149-4	PACIFIC FISH
No. 150-8	COLONIES	No. 105-2	SHARKS
No. 151-6	PIONEERS	No. 106-0	WHALES
No. 154-0	FARM ANIMALS	No. 107-9	DEEP-SEA FISH
No. 095-1	DOLLS	No. 108-7	DOLPHINS
No. 096-X	ANIMAL ALPHABET	No. 109-5	AIRCRAFT
No. 160-5	CATS	No. 110-9	SPACE CRAFT

No. 111-7	SPACE EXPLORERS
No. 112-5	PLANETS
No. 113-3	COMETS
No. 114-1	ROCKETS
No. 155-9	TRANSPORTATION
No. 156-7	SHIPS

LISTEN AND COLOR
LIBRARY ALBUMS
6 BOOKS & STORY CASSETTES
in a plastic storage case

We have gathered cassettes and books of related subject matter into individual library albums. Each album will provide a new, in-depth and lasting learning experience. They are presented in a beautiful binder that will store and protect your collection for years.
We also invite you to select 6 titles and create a CUSTOM ALBUM.

CHOOSE ANY LIBRARY ALBUM LISTED, OR SELECT TITLES FOR YOUR CUSTOM ALBUM

No. 088-9 Prehistoric Life	No. 116-8 American Indian	No. 164-8 Oceans & Seas	No. 117-6 Air & Space	No. 165-6 Americana
Dinosaurs	Plains Indians	Atlantic Fish	Aircraft	Colonies
Prehistoric Sea Life	Northeast Indians	Pacific Fish	Space Craft	Cowboys
Prehistoric Fish	Northwest Indians	Sharks	Space Explorers	Pioneers
Prehistoric Birds	Southeast Indians	Whales	Planets	State Flowers
Prehistoric Mammals	Southwest Indians	Deep-Sea Fish	Comets	State Birds
Cave Man	California Indians	Dolphins	Rockets	Endangered Species

No. 166-4 Animal Libr #1	No. 167-2 Animal Libr. #2	No. 168-0 Young Students	No. 170-2 New Titles Library	No. 169-9 Custom Library
Poisonous Snakes	Prehistoric Mammals	Animal Alphabet	Eskimos	**WE INVITE YOU TO PICK 6 TITLES OF YOUR CHOOSING TO CREATE YOUR OWN CUSTOM LIBRARY.**
Reptiles	Birds	Counting & Coloring Dinosaurs	State Flowers	
Animal Giants	Farm Animals	Dolls	Penguins	
Mammals	Endangered Species	Dogs	Atlantic Fish	
Cats of the Wild	Animal Alphabet	Cats	Pacific Fish	
Primates	State Birds	Horses	Farm Animals	